Criticality Analysis Made Simple

by
Tacoma Zach, P.Eng, CRL

Criticality Analysis
Made Simple
by
Tacoma Zach, P.Eng, CRL

ISBN 978-1-941872-26-0
HF112020

Publisher: Reliabilityweb.com
Layout Design: Apolonia Lemus
Cover Design: Jocelyn Brown

For information: Reliabilityweb.com
www.reliabilityweb.com
8991 Daniels Center Drive, Suite 105, Ft. Myers, FL 33912
Toll Free: 888-575-1245 | Phone: 239-333-2500
E-mail: crm@reliabilityweb.com

10   9   8   7

Dedication

This book is dedicated first to my good friend and asset management mentor, Terry Nelson. Without Terry's passion for asset management, his friendly influence and encyclopedic knowledge of all things AM, this whole journey with criticality analysis would never have happened. His decency, generosity of time, and knowledge is greatly appreciated. Terry saw where asset management needed to go decades before the industry did, and was influential in directing the course in asset management for one of the biggest water companies in the world. It was great to have courtside seats for that. He is a true 'visioneer.'

I am also compelled, without reservation, to thank my wife and chief editor without whose tireless struggle with an engineer to make this book more accessible, intelligible, and just plain better, this book would have remained an idea, and would not have had the means to be accomplished. Thank you for making me better.

Preface

The first time I participated in a criticality analysis I was the West Regional Manager for Veolia Water and we were doing an analysis at one of our sites within a large refinery in California. We operated a high purity boiler feed water facility and we knew we were at risk in some areas. A colleague had been doing some great work in criticality analysis with impressive results and I decided that it would be a good idea to do an analysis at this site. We had a pretty clear picture of where we were at risk and were planning to replace some large, expensive pressure vessels showing obvious signs of corrosion. We expected the analysis to affirm this and support our capital expenditure.

Through the criticality analysis, much to our surprise, we discovered that our greatest risk and most critical system were not the expensive pressure vessels. Instead, an inexpensive brine pumping system had the potential to shut us down within 8 hours of failure, putting the entire refinery boiler operation at risk. We could mitigate this significant risk with a combination of a new replacement and a standby, and only spend 1/1000 of the money we were planning to spend.

Further, at least 30 % of the major risks we identified that week had remained undiscovered for almost 2 decades of operation, including significant business risk. The client and our whole team were blown away – and relieved that we had discovered these actual risks.

Flash forward. I now own Uberlytics, the company that grew out of many years of those experiences; we specialize in criticality analysis tools and consulting. (I guess you could say I liked it so much, I bought the company.) We are passionate about helping organizations discover what is most critical to their corporate mission and help them use that information to optimize not only their asset management programs, but also improve their safety, operations, environmental, risk management programs, and more.

Through our work with organizations we see two big challenges facing asset management and reliability engineering programs today: **knowing where to start and setting priorities.**

Rhys Davies, Chairman of the ISO Committee PC251, recently made this observation in Uptime Magazine:

I have worked in so many organizations where engineering teams have not been provided with the necessary clarity on what they should be achieving. This results in enthusiastic and capable engineers trying to improve things in a world where they are fighting for resources among a myriad of other initiatives. It is not always possible to see how our reliability initiatives fit into the bigger picture, nor how we can defend our positions. (*ISO55000: It's All About the Value*, Uptime Magazine, Dec/Jan14)

I am 100% convinced that a criticality analysis is key to solving the challenge of clarity on what is to be achieved, establishing priorities, and aligning and targeting resources. A criticality analysis is the starting point for making sure everyone is working towards achieving better outcomes.

Our intention is to make criticality analysis simple to understand and easier to apply through this book. Our goal is to help you do the right thing, in the right order, for the right reasons, to get the right results. The concepts and approach we outline here have been proven to be highly effective and very efficient in multiple organizations. We know that they can be effective for you too.

Tacoma Zach, P.Eng, CRL
September 2014

Table of Contents

Understanding Criticality

Chapter 1: What Is Criticality?
Chapter 2: Why Is a Criticality Analysis Important?
Chapter 3: Where Does a Criticality Analysis
Fit in Your Asset Management
Program?

What Is Criticality?

February 2, 2013, was a historic night at the Mercedes-Benz Superdome in New Orleans. The Baltimore Ravens and San Francisco 49ers, both undefeated in previous championship games, were vying to be the Super Bowl XLVII champions.

After an electric half-time show, the Ravens looked to be on their way to a decisive victory. As the second-half started, Jacoby Jones returned the opening kick-off for a 108-yard touchdown, the longest play ever in Super Bowl or post-season history. The Ravens were now leading the 49ers 28-6.

Then, with 13:22 left to play in the third quarter, the lights went out - the first stadium blackout in Super Bowl history.

Something critical had failed.

Every day facilities and operations are striving to avoid failure, mitigate risk and maximize uptime – striving to deliver value from their assets toward their objectives. Organizations turn to asset management and reliability engineering programs to optimize their efforts. The stakes are high and resources are limited.

Knowledge about your systems and assets and their impact on organizational objectives and managing risk is vital. The overall success of an asset management program rides on the quality of the decisions that are made in establishing priorities and allocating resources. Quality decisions depend on having quality information and truly knowing where your limited resources have to be applied first.

Understanding the true criticality of your systems and assets will enable you to intelligently prioritize and align your asset management and reliability engineering initiatives and resources. A criticality analysis is a key starting point for acquiring the knowledge and decision support you need to get the best results from your asset management and reliability engineering programs.

Understanding Criticality

Criticality is a measure of the relative importance of something, usually a tangible system or asset, to the corporate mission, objectives and values of your organization. Often the criticality of a particular asset is obvious, but sometimes it is not and will only be discovered through an intentional process called a criticality analysis.

A **criticality analysis** is a way to determine which systems and assets are most essential, in order to set priorities for further reliability initiatives and deeper analysis.

This analysis is a means of examining and understanding available data; collecting and preserving organizational knowledge; understanding the effect of a failure of a system or some part or whole of an asset; evaluating the severity of the resulting consequences; ascribing a likelihood to the failure occurring; and then organizing all of this information to compare and rank the results.

From the risk side, a criticality analysis is designed to identify what can upset or interfere with the objectives and values of an organization or facility: what can shut you down, result in a discharge to the environment, hurt someone, result in fines, terminate a contract, miss financial targets, etc.

On the positive side, the analysis identifies where you must pay attention and devote resources in order to meet all your objectives.

When we understand what is critical, we can set priorities for delivering value from assets. These priorities then direct where to focus asset management activities for reliability engineering, asset condition management and work execution management.

Some Common Misperceptions About Criticality

There is some potential for confusion when discussing criticality as it relates to asset management, reliability and risk identification.

Some people and processes use the word **criticality** to

Are we speaking the same language?

crit•i•cal•i•ty /kritəˈkalitē/

1. The quality, state, or degree of being of the highest importance.
2. Having a decisive or crucial importance in the success, failure, or existence of something.

refer to the condition of an asset or the likelihood of an imminent failure. This leads to some misunderstanding of the nature of something being critical.

When discussing criticality and criticality analysis in the context of an organization, we are talking about discovering the relative importance of systems and assets to the overall mission and objectives: **What systems and assets are essential for this organization to meet its mission objectives?**

We are looking to identify the most vital parts but sometimes this gets mixed up with some common misperceptions about criticality. Here are several we encounter regularly.

We know what is most critical already, so we don't need to do a criticality analysis.

This is probably the most common objection to conducting a criticality analysis. We often encounter operations personnel who are certain they 'know what is critical'. This is almost true – they often do know about 80% of what is critical. But what about the 20% that is unknown? And, after some discussion, we might discover that their criticality rankings are based on an older or skewed mission statement, which does not align with the current organizational aim or mission.

Or, too often, we come across rankings that are really just numbers plucked out of the air, based on a good hunch. This finger-in-the-wind approach leads to real-life examples like a kitchen appliance in the break room having the same criticality ranking as a key piece of process equipment in a refinery. Inevitably, through a proper criticality analysis we find something very critical that has been overlooked, or resources being misdirected to non-critical assets.

It is also important to ask **who** in your facility "knows" what is critical. How is their knowledge being preserved? What happens if they leave or get hit by a bus? A criticality analysis will integrate, document and preserve vital institutional knowledge.

Are you relying on a hunch or assumption that your organization truly understands the criticality of your systems and assets?

An expensive asset is definitely a critical asset. (Something inexpensive can't be that critical.)

Have you ever been sidelined by a faulty tire valve? A fifty-cent part can make you late for work or miss your plane. However, it's doubtful a rip in your expensive leather upholstery ever kept your car from getting you where you needed to go.

It is very easy to think that if an asset is expensive, it must be critical and therefore deserves lots of attention. While expensive items certainly should be looked after well, as the alternative is costly, they are not automatically critical.

Conversely, it is often assumed that an inexpensive part is unimportant. It is not uncommon that a small part or cheap system (like a seal water system) can have a major effect on the overall mission.

Are you paying undue attention to expensive assets or overlooking something important?

If something is in poor condition, then it is critical.

Confusing condition with criticality is an easy and common mistake – we speak of things being in critical condition all the time, meaning doing poorly. The condition of an asset does not correlate with its criticality to the function or mission of the system. To be sure, the condition of an asset affects the likelihood of its failure, but it does not change its importance to your operation.

Criticality analysis is different from condition assessment, which falls in the domain of Asset Condition Management. Criticality analysis combined with condition assessment and management is essential for directing work planning and execution.

Are you distracted by the condition of assets that are not critical to your operation?

We just did a HAZOP/FMEA/FMECA so we don't need another analysis. We've got all the information we need.

These studies take a lot of hard work. However, they have different aims and deliver different information than a criticality analysis.

A failure mode effects analysis (FMEA) is a bottom-up inductive analysis. It starts at the asset level and is focused on asset performance, the ways an asset can fail and the effects of failure on its performance. An FMEA does not tell you how important an asset is to the mission of your facility. A failure mode effects and criticality analysis (FMECA) is an extension of an FMEA and is a step closer. While it includes a criticality component, in strict terms the criticality part is focused on the importance of the failure effect on performance. The objective is to determine which failure brings about the worse case performance. Both an FMEA and FMECA are inwardly focused on asset performance analysis, and start from the bottom up.

Here's the bad news: if you completed an FMEA or FMECA without having a criticality analysis, you may have just wasted resources. A system criticality analysis prior to the FMEA will help you target your resources first toward systems and assets that are most critical to sustaining your operation.

Similarly, a Hazardous Operability (HAZOP) study does not help you identify your most important assets. A HAZOP evaluates process safety engineering design to identify inherent hazards to safe operation and functionality. A HAZOP can tell you when the wrong valve is selected for design inclusion but not how important that valve is.

In contrast to the FMEA, FMECA and the HAZOP, a system criticality analysis starts with the big picture of your operation, evaluates the importance of systems and their assets to the corporate mission and facility objectives and considers the consequences of failure to reaching these mission objectives. The criticality rankings then direct further reliability engineering activities like FMEAs, FMECAs, capital project management or preventive maintenance (PM) optimization.

Is a safety hazard being mistaken for a critical asset? Are you wasting valuable resources on non-critical assets?

A criticality analysis is a very expensive and time-consuming effort. We're not sure it's worth the effort.

Like anything else in operations, a criticality analysis can easily be done inefficiently and cost way too much. However, an effective criticality analysis can be accomplished with far less time and cost than you may anticipate. In the following chapters we will show you how to set up your analysis, gather the right people and resources, use the best tools and where to begin, all in order to get the best value from your analysis.

It is possible to dramatically reduce the workload and time required and at the same time improve the quality of your analysis. Don't let the perceived short-term cost of a criticality analysis prevent you from taking advantage of all the long-term benefits it will bring.

Summary

Criticality is a measure of the relative importance of systems and assets to the corporate mission, objectives and values of your organization. A criticality analysis discovers which systems and assets are most essential to your corporate mission, and helps set priorities for further reliability initiatives and deeper analysis.

Through the discussion of common misperceptions about criticality, the value of a criticality analysis has started to become apparent. Next, we will look deeper into why a criticality analysis is important.

Why Is a Criticality Analysis Important?

A criticality analysis will inform and influence many of your other reliability initiatives. Truly understanding the criticality of your systems and assets allows for mitigating risk, directs further reliability engineering efforts, fine tunes asset condition management, improves work execution management and lays the foundation for aligning all activities toward the mission of your organization.

In this chapter we outline some of the key general benefits of a system criticality analysis. Additional benefits and advantages will be discussed later in Section 3.

Key Benefits
- Alignment
- Decision Support
- Identifying Risk
- Safety and Criticality

Alignment

Most people will agree that it is important to know what is important. However, the definition of what is important may vary from person to person, which results in misalignment of objectives, priorities and execution.

An asset management program involves lots of people and multiple departments. Success requires aligning all these people and departments toward delivery of the organization's mission and objectives. This alignment requires common understanding and agreement on what is really important or critical to meeting the mission.

The collaborative and cross-functional nature of a criticality analysis brings together all the stakeholders, analyzes and integrates valuable data from organizational silos and delivers coherent information for establishing priorities that everyone can agree to.

Decision Support

When implementing an asset management program decisions have to be made about where to spend limited resources. Properly conducting an FMEA on all equipment in a facility is not generally feasible. Nor is it usually tenable to measure every motor vibration in real time continuously, to analyze oil from every gearbox, or to get up to date condition assessments for every piece of equipment.

Economic pressures and shareholder value demand that funds only be spent on what is essential to deliver value from the assets, mitigate risk, and deliver return on investment.

As we stated earlier the success of a program depends on how well these decisions are made. The results of the criticality analysis deliver the support necessary for making the best decisions and can set the direction for all facets of asset management and reliability programs.

Figure 1

A criticality analysis identifies your critical systems and assets, supports making decisions about where to focus condition assessment or monitoring activities and further analysis, and underpins agreement on those priorities.

Identifying Risk

A criticality analysis done correctly will identify risk. Knowing what systems and assets can upset the mission objectives, put people at risk, and expose the company to other risks is vital.

Defining and identifying risk depends on the defined objectives and criteria for meeting the company mission and what is considered important by management and shareholders. This expands the idea of risk beyond just uptime, safety or environmental. Other areas of risk include production efficiency, quality, commercial terms, compliance or exposure to litigation.

A well-planned criticality assessment will provide the appropriate level of granularity to identify and form the basis for mitigating those risks, which can lead to further benefits.

Safety and Criticality

A criticality analysis can have a profound impact on safety. From a maintenance perspective, anytime we invasively address an asset we raise the risk of infant mortality (equipment failure shortly after startup) and other introduced failures. This also applies to safety of personnel. Anytime a piece of equipment must be handled in a way that goes beyond just inspecting or non-invasively monitoring it, personnel safety risk is elevated. Anything beyond normal operating procedures raises the risk level of something unintended happening.

Our experience shows that non-routine events account for a large share of safety incidents. From a safety point of view, focusing invasive and high-risk activities on more critical systems and assets is a sound and proven approach to managing safety risk. This will result in an improvement in the overall safety record, and a commensurate improvement in overall risk profile.

Summary

A criticality analysis will deliver value in a multitude of ways including alignment of stakeholders, foundational decision support for directing asset management activities, and risk identification and mitigation.

From this brief outline of general benefits, we see that understanding criticality and implementing a criticality analysis will have an impact throughout your organization. Next, we look at how and where criticality fits into the big picture of your operation.

Where Does a Criticality Analysis Fit in Your Asset Management Program?

Understanding criticality in your organization is an integral part of your overall asset management (am) program and will influence all stages of the asset management timeline.

Criticality should influence **design**, in not only the kind of equipment selected for reliability but also in designing the interrelationship of systems to accommodate for the potential impact that failure of one system can have on other systems and the overall facility.

Criticality is central to the creation of a **reliability and maintenance plan** once a facility is in operation. A planned periodic review of criticality will be important as the need for process and equipment upgrades and changes becomes apparent.

Criticality will sharply focus the needs for **upgrades and modifications** to reduce unacceptable risks and improve reliability. It targets and prioritizes limited capital and refurbishment budgets.

Timing of a Criticality Analysis

The first opportunity to do a criticality analysis is during the design phase of a facility. At this stage additional design modifications and equipment selections can be implemented to reduce the number of high-risk assets, or level of consequences.

Performing a criticality analysis at the beginning will influence and set future maintenance needs, and help achieve the lowest cost of ownership from the outset.

Ideally, a criticality analysis will be one of the first steps taken when establishing an asset management and reliability engineering program in order to reap the benefits of superior plant performance and optimized cost from the start. In addition, building an archive of historical asset data is extremely valuable for future decisions.

Of course, we rarely work in an ideal world and many mature organizations will already be deep in asset management programs without having criticality data. In this case, it is desirable to start a criticality analysis as soon as possible.

For a facility that is already in the operational and maintenance phase the benefits will be realized immediately as adjustments to PMs, work planning, capital budgets, human resources and more can be made. In short order the impact of the criticality analysis will be widespread with the net result of overall greater resource efficiency, plant performance improvement, and plant risk profile reduction.

Companies with multiple facilities can start with just one location. The learning from this first analysis can then be leveraged and applied to similar situations at other facilities, taking care to adjust for specific local context.

Once an initial analysis is complete, there needs to be a plan in place for maintaining and re-evaluating the criticality analysis process to reflect any subsequent changes in design, equipment or objectives which influence criticality rankings.

Criticality and the Domains of Asset Management

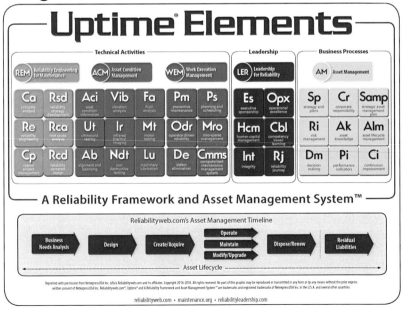

Figure 2 Uptime® Elements

Understanding the criticality of your systems and assets is foundational to all four domains of the reliability system as detailed in Uptime Elements™:

- Reliability Engineering for Maintenance
- Asset Condition Management
- Work Execution Management
- Leadership for Reliability

In each of these domains there are activities that are vital to the success of your reliability programs. However, it would be overwhelming and cost-prohibitive to apply all of these activities to all of your assets.

A criticality analysis will allow you to do the right things, in the right order, for the right reasons, to get the right results.

Reliability Engineering for Maintenance (REM)

REM activities like failure mode effects analysis (FMEA) or reliability centered maintenance (RCM) are important but not practical to apply to all of your assets. One of the first things a criticality analysis does is identify which **systems** are most critical to your operation. By starting at the system level instead of down at the asset level, you can very quickly focus REM activities on only your most critical systems and the assets in them, improving efficiency and reducing cost.

The recently published **Reliability Centered Maintenance (RCM) Project Manager's Guide** (2014 Reliabilityweb.com) says the first essential element of an RCM project is that "the RCM is performed on a system that is composed of components that together provide an **important, and even essential, function to the organization.**" It goes on to recommend a no-go decision if there is not sufficient data to select a candidate system for RCM analysis.

In the same way, there is no point in wasting the time and resources required for an FMEA or PM optimization on non-critical assets, as the benefit derived will be negligible. Further, the need to conduct root cause analyses (RCA) should be reduced if the criticality effort has had its influence on the other elements because failures should be reduced. In fact, RCA may also be considered optional for lower mid to low critical systems and assets in the event of failure, as their impact is actually negligible.

When a criticality analysis precedes other REM initiatives, there will be significant cost savings and efficiencies as well as greater benefits to be found.

Asset Condition Management (ACM)

Similarly, ACM activities can be expensive, time consuming, require high resource allocations - and are extremely important. The need to focus resources for the greatest return on investment is paramount.

Condition assessments like vibration analysis, oil analysis, infrared and ultrasound testing can absorb a large chunk of the yearly budget. It is important not to waste money on low critical items, yet it is vital to track the condition of critical assets.

For example, you would not apply these assessments to a sump pump in a non-critical plant system, but you would definitely need to assess the main feed pumps in a plant.

This is less obvious when mid-critical assets comprise the bulk of your facility. A criticality analysis will help you identify where you need condition assessments most, resulting in large savings of time and resources.

Work Execution Management (WEM)

Work execution management will be directly linked to the criticality analysis results.

Preventive maintenance activities will be influenced by criticality rankings. Non-critical items that can be run to failure don't need the same attention as those assets that cannot 'go down.'

Planning and scheduling must be prioritized by both work order priority **and** criticality ranking. This avoids mixed up priorities like painting a critical item when a mid-critical asset is making noise, or fixing a non-critical broken pump that could be out of service for weeks with no measurable impact, instead of addressing a hot bearing on a more critical pump.

Criticality can also influence the selection and implementation of a CMMS system. Fields must be available in a CMMS system to accommodate and use criticality numbers to influence work orders.

Leadership for Reliability (LER)

Again, all the elements in this domain are affected by understanding the criticality of your systems first.

Operational excellence will be more easily achieved when wasteful spending on unimportant tasks and assets are eliminated. Human resources can be targeted toward assets of greatest concern. Competency based learning must, at its core focus on critical assets, and so on.

A criticality analysis is especially valuable for gaining executive sponsorship for reliability initiatives or capital projects. When executives know that resources are being directed toward the most important assets for meeting the aims of the facility and the company, it will be much easier to get their support.

Finally, making sure that a true understanding of criticality underpins your asset management and reliability program embodies one of the most important elements of all - integrity.

You need integrity to want to know what is important and where limited resources should be spent, integrity to recognize and lay aside pet projects, and integrity to conduct an analysis that is true, verifiable, defensible and accurate, that will stand under rigorous scrutiny. Integrity does the right things for the right reasons in a responsible and efficient manner, eliminating wasted and unnecessary efforts.

Summary

In this first section we defined criticality and addressed some common misperceptions like confusing condition with criticality and thinking that a criticality analysis will be too expensive or time consuming to implement.

Next, we asked why criticality is important and identified some key benefits of a criticality analysis, like aligning stakeholders and departments toward delivery of organizational objectives and delivering quality data to inform quality decisions.

Finally, we discussed where a criticality analysis fits into an overall asset management plan and how understanding criticality will influence and support activities in every domain of your AM program.

We introduced this section with the stadium blackout during the 2013 Super Bowl. It was later determined that the Super Bowl power failure was caused by the "mis-operation" of a relay device, which was part of the electric switchgear bringing power into the station. Ironically, this equipment had been recently installed during upgrades prior to the stadium hosting the Super Bowl.

In this case, the power company and stadium officials "knew" that the lines coming into the stadium were critical so they took the step of upgrading the equipment. But, among other procedural activities that were missed, it would seem that the true criticality of the system's parts and components were not properly understood nor reviewed. The result was an expensive and embarrassing blackout on a very public stage.

You may not be at risk of being embarrassed in front of millions on national television on a Sunday night.

Likely, the stakes are much higher and the risks more significant in your operation.

Through understanding criticality and implementing a criticality analysis, you will be taking important steps toward avoiding these risks. In the following section we will discuss how to put this into action.

Section 2

How to Implement an Effective Criticality Analysis

Key Elements of an Effective Criticality Analysis

An effective criticality analysis:

- Efficiently identifies the systems and assets in your operation that can impact the stated goals and objectives of the company or facility.
- Is agreed to by all represented/participating stakeholder groups in the analysis.
- Delivers detailed results that are actionable on a system and asset level.
- Is documented sufficiently so that it can be audited at a later date with little ambiguity as to why choices and determinations were made.
- Provides a meaningfully ranked order of results.

There are several key elements that will help you successfully complete a criticality analysis that meets these objectives. Make sure these elements are in place and/or understood prior to starting your analysis:

1. **Leadership** support and participation
2. Clear understanding of **facility mission objectives**
3. Well-defined **categories** for evaluating criticality
4. Well-organized **asset hierarchy**
5. Starting from a **system-level approach**

Leadership

As in any asset management and reliability program, effective leadership will be key to the success of a criticality analysis. In particular, both executive leadership and local operational leadership are required.

Senior leadership, support and participation are essential to any endeavor that hopes to be successful at a plant-wide level and to set the course for all maintenance and capital related activities. Without executive sponsorship the best laid plans will be sidelined and very little will get done. Leadership from the top of an organization will also help align the organization with the line-of-sight requirements of ISO55001.

Executive leadership will be required to set the resources aside for analysis expenses and will help maintain the momentum and focus required to complete the effort. Senior leadership should also plan to measure the ROI over the course of the next few years. Expected results will be:

- Improved risk profile
- Sharpened budget focus
- Sharpened application of personnel resources
- Improved KPIs in all areas of interest
- Improved safety and reliability culture
- A more robust and resilient business that delivers higher shareholder value

Leadership is also needed at the plant and operational level to organize and implement the analysis. A successful and actionable criticality analysis requires a leadership commitment to achieve consensus, to put aside pet projects and allow the data to show which systems and assets actually jeopardize stated goals and objectives, from personnel safety through commercial terms.

One of the biggest challenges we see in organizations is getting all the stakeholders and participants on the same page and moving in the same direction. Cross-functional participation is extremely important. Effective leadership will bring the right people together, help them understand the process and the value of it, and move them forward. The goal at the end is staff consensus on the criticality rankings, aligning activities across functional groups like maintenance and operations.

One of the first steps in this process is making sure everyone understands and agrees on the facility objectives.

Facility Objectives

Clearly stated mission objectives and goals are foundational to uncovering critical systems and assets in your organization. These objectives and goals will be defined by multiple factors and constraints beyond uptime or production.

Most organizations have a general idea of what is critical to their operation. However, this knowledge is often based on opinion or perception rather than on actual risk, and is usually limited to production objectives or uptime. Typically, only about 80% of the assets that are vital to keeping the plant running have been properly identified.

While uptime and production are extremely important there are other objectives and contributing factors that can easily be overlooked. An organization usually has multiple stakeholders from investors and stockholders, local government, regulators, public relations and senior management right on down to the functional groups at the plant level, who actually get the work done and have their own priorities.

The priorities of the group you represent in your company are not likely to be the same as another group's priorities. The equipment important to keeping the plant running is not necessarily what is required to keep operators out of harm's way, or to maintain an acceptable level of environmental or regulatory risk. There will be overlap of course, but there are unique systems and assets related to different priorities. How will competing priorities be ranked and managed?

A clear understanding of your corporate objectives is essential to the success of the criticality analysis. What are the stated goals and mission of your organization, public or private? What is important to the Board of Directors, the town council, and the senior management? Without a clearly defined set of objectives or clearly defined mission statement, a criticality analysis, no matter how well executed, will not deliver results reflective of the organization's needs, and will ultimately reduce the potential ROI on the whole asset management (AM) program.

Corporate objectives have to be carefully considered in preparation for performing a criticality analysis. The outlook of your analysis needs to be broader than simply minimizing downtime or maximizing throughout.

We find it helpful to explain some of the concepts of criticality and elements of an analysis in the context of a car. Think of your family minivan: what is the objective of this vehicle? There are several likely purposes that your car serves:

- Get you to and from work each day reliably
- Safely transport your children to school
- Provide transportation for family recreation and vacation

Now imagine that you are the owner of a restored Shelby Cobra that you show on the classic car show circuit. In this scenario objectives of the vehicle change a little:

- Win Best in Class
- Vintage Auto Racing
- Pleasure and pride of ownership

When the objective or purpose of your vehicle changes, your priorities for its maintenance and operation change. These priorities are analogous to the evaluation categories you will use in your criticality analysis.

Evaluation Categories

From clearly stated mission and objectives you will then be able to identify and define the criteria or categories you will use to evaluate the criticality of your systems and assets.

As we have noted, the viability of an organization depends on more than production uptime. In preparing for an analysis, many categories of evaluation must be considered for inclusion. In addition to production capacity and quality other categories would be safety, environmental, regulatory, commercial terms, public perception or relations, stakeholder impact, and more.

Here are some examples of evaluation categories:

Safety

Staff safety is an obvious category to be included in the analysis. There is also public safety to consider. In many public utility operations there are times crews have to go into the community to repair a failed asset, with commensurate disruption to traffic or public access. Industrial facilities can be surrounded by residential communities, posing a risk to the general population.

Environmental

There may be potential environmental risks to avoid, particularly when dealing with sensitive surrounding areas or the potential to contaminate receiving waters or ground, such as a public wastewater facility or even a refinery. Environmental discharges might also include a cross over to public safety if the public has a chance of contacting the discharge as in a sewer overflow, discharge violation to receiving streams, or an oil spill on or off immediate property (pipelines or railways). In a public utility scenario, Public Health is usually the crossover area.

Regulatory

Regulatory compliance, such as in a consent decree or air monitoring requirements, is the often-overlooked cousin of environmental discharge because it is more subtle and less visible to the public. Not considering regulatory compliance can seriously impact an organization. A refinery, for example, has several emission control operations within its boundaries. Regular monitoring of the exhaust gases is generally a requirement of the applicable permit to operate. While all exhaust gases might be within the acceptable range, if the frequency of sampling is lower than that specified in the permit, a serious violation might be levied, and can result in additional financial and resource burdens imposed on the operation like a shutdown, as well as negative press and PR damage to the company or management. Depending on the region of the country or the current public perception of a company, these may be very unwelcome risks and should be considered in the analysis.

Commercial Terms

Commercial terms are also often overlooked in lieu of production or uptime and can carry additional impact to the overall operation beyond lost production volume. For example, the terms of a contract with a service provider within the larger confines of a client facility often carry liquidated damages, or financial obligations to cover the cost of alternate delivery options to the customer. Litigation might also be invoked in the event of certain trigger events, that might not be limited to quantity, but also quality or timeliness.

In determining your final list of evaluation categories, the current list of key performance indicators (KPIs) that measure facility performance will also have bearing on what to include. Your final list must be comprehensive and reflective of the current state of affairs, but not too large to be unmanageable. Ideally, you should aim for a list of five to eight evaluation categories. To accomplish this some criteria can be grouped together. How this is done will depend on the local context and the needs of your organization. It is important to give a final review of the categories, as they should not be modified once the analysis starts. Early in the analysis process you will rank these categories relative to each other, often referred to as weighting the category.

Minivan Objective: Reliably and safely get me to work.
Evaluation Categories:
- Reliability: not overheat in the summer
- Visibility: let me see well out of the windows on a slushy highway
- Versatility: let me drive at night
- Safety: must let me connect to my phone via blue tooth

Restored Shelby Cobra Objective: Win Best in Class
Evaluation Categories:
- Appearance: have the best restored paint, highest polish on chrome
- Originality: have the most original parts
- Performance: does what it advertises

These categories help you determine where you will spend your budget on maintaining your car and which maintenance activities are the most important.

Defining Severity

It is very important to define levels of severity of adverse events to help the analysis run smoothly and quickly. The definitions of each level of severity must be unique from one another, but should be applicable across multiple categories. We refer to them as Impact Descriptions to focus on the impact a level of severity has.

The severity of adverse events will usually be defined in a range of 5-6 levels that starts with No Impact and ends with Catastrophe or Intolerable. We find it helpful to use colors to visually convey severity. A worst case or catastrophe is represented by red, while a tolerable event is green or blue, with a range of colors in between.

Where possible have definitions for the different levels that are similar for each category. So a 'red-level' definition for safety could be the same as a 'red-level' for environmental. The definitions should focus on three important factors: the rate at which the impact happens (helps determine if you can intervene before hand), the severity of the impact, and the ability to mitigate the consequences. The graphic illustrates a sample of the type of definition that can be applied to any category at any time.

Impact Descriptions

	Impacts are immediate, severe, and cannot be mitigated
	Major Impacts are immediate, mitigation is limited
	Significant Impacts can occur quickly or accumulate, mitigation is possible
	Moderate Impacts, can accumulate and can be mitigated
	Impacts are minor

Figure 3

Normalizing definitions across categories and making them applicable over time will be very useful. This means that something like a change in sensitivity to cost would not require a redefinition or re-doing of the analysis. A definition of a severe event, for example, should also be consistent from region to region, even country to country to facilitate corporate wide comparisons.

Since this analysis will be revisited on a regular basis the level of severity of a consequence should be somewhat time-independent to be able to compare the analysis over time.

Generic descriptions of severity levels are preferable to severity defined by something like cost or quantity of an event. Financial thresholds will change over time so it is better not to include financial numbers related to impacts. For example, you would not want to define a severe impact as one that costs $100,000.00. A severe dollar-value impact today may not be considered as severe 5 years from now. Conversely, a moderate impact, easily mitigated today might pose a far greater challenge in 10 years. Similarly so for changing regulations - try to avoid hard numbers that will change over time.

The value of having a limited number of definitions that are consistent across several categories is the ability of the participants to recall the definitions, and the consistency of scale across the categories. The severity of an impact in the environmental category will be more easily compared and scaled to an impact in production capacity.

Organizing Your Assets

Prior to starting your criticality analysis you will need a complete asset hierarchy, which is different than an asset register. First, we look at the register.

Asset Register

An asset register is a list of all the assets at a facility. The most common issue we encounter is incomplete asset registers. This is due to several reasons including failing to start building the asset register at the design and construction phase. Most often we come across registers that do not include pipes and valves, a significant financial investment.

Often the comment is made that there are too many assets to deal with effectively in the CMMS, so they limit the register to only what they normally write work orders for. This just compounds the issue.

A 100% complete asset register is essential to any criticality analysis, and in fact any AM program. If something is part of the process, if it can affect the operation in any way, if it has any chance of contributing to safety issues, environmental containment, regulatory compliance, legal requirements, commercial issues, if it was ever paid for, then it needs to be in the asset register.

So every pipe, valve, sensor, and instrument needs to be part of the register. It should be done at the beginning or when the register is created to maintain uniformity of coding, description, and organization. Later additions should be limited and controlled by select team members, as this often creates duplicates or corrupts the structure. (Of course, some additions will be necessary with items like replacement valves, pipes, sensors and other high count items.)

Including every asset can be a daunting task. This challenge can be overcome by using group assets.

Group Assets

Through grouping like assets within a functional system you can simplify your register while still including 100% of your assets. For example, count all the sections of pipe in a system as a group asset. The pipe as a group will then be used in the evaluation. The same principle can then apply to all the valves or field sensors or field installed instruments in a system: capture and treat them as a group asset.

There are several advantages to this for other aspects of an AM program, but those are beyond the scope of this work, other than to say it is a tremendous help in capturing cost data and work order management. Note that there will be occasions where a sensor, or valve, or meter must be pulled out from the group list for regulatory reasons, or even asset criticality reasons, but this is easily accomplished once the overall register is complete.

Consistent Asset Definitions

It is important that every team member has the same idea of what an asset is in contrast to a system or a component. Ensure that the register is consistent in what constitutes an asset. By this we mean assets are listed at the asset level, and components of assets are not, nor are systems listed at the asset level.

For example a chemical feed system is listed on the system level. A pump in this system is listed on the asset level, regardless of size. The wet end of this pump is listed as a component or sub-asset.

A Note on Asset Codes and Types

It's important to have a clear code structure on asset types. Codes should be consistent in length on the asset level, unique (databases do not do well with duplicates) and if possible, reflect the parent relationships of the asset (see Asset Hierarchies next.)

When identifying assets it is generally useful to distinguish between different types of the same class of assets. A system may have multiple pumps as assets but not all pumps are the same type. A vertical turbine is a different sort of pump than a horizontal centrifugal pump, with different failure modes and therefore different maintenance needs. Likewise, a rotameter is a different flow measurement asset than a magnetic flow meter. They are both flow meter assets, but are different asset types, again with different implications for maintenance. Here are some examples of unique codes for different types of an asset class, in this case pumps:

PMPVERT – Vertical Turbine Pump
PMPCENH – Horizontal Centrifugal Pump
PMPCENV – Vertical Centrifugal Pump

A clear code structure will be extremely useful for extracting very specific information from the data base for analysis, risk mitigation, potential redesign, general AM financial detail analysis and, of course, future maintenance programs based on failure modes.

Asset Hierarchy

An asset hierarchy is an asset register organized in a way that is meaningful and useful to your organization.

Different departments may have different preferences for how they organize a hierarchy. Accounting departments usually group assets by geography or what building it is in, including the building as an asset. Their focus is usually depreciation, and where an asset exists in the world.

Maintenance and operations professionals, who have responsibility to keep the plant running, need a different way of organizing things. We highly recommend organizing an asset hierarchy by grouping assets that are related to a specific function or purpose regardless of location.

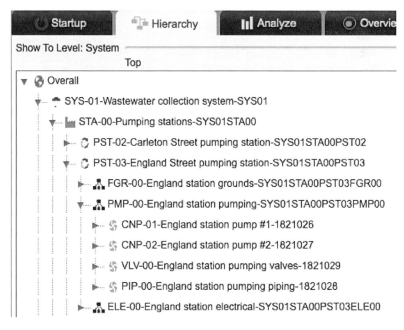

Figure 4

This means every asset is part of a system, each system is part of a collection of systems that could be called processes, which are then collectively part of a collection of processes perhaps grouped by wet, solid, and support trains or areas of the plant. The nomenclature above the system level is not that important here and depends on what works at your facility.

A functional system-based hierarchy can look like this:

- A plant has several process areas,
  - Δ those process areas contain several functional systems,
    - those systems are made of several assets,

    • each asset is made up of several components like shafts and bearings
        • and on down it goes until you get to ball bearings, housings, pins etc.
These levels are generally described as parent-child relationships. More complex plants and systems will have more parent-child levels in their hierarchy. The parent-child ratio should hover around 1 to 7, with ratios greater than 1 to 10 being the exception as determined by the actual plant design.

There are key reasons a hierarchy, and specifically a **functional system-based hierarchy**, is extremely important for a criticality analysis, and asset management in general:

- It makes finding assets extremely easy, in contrast to lumping everything into large buckets based on accounting, location or type.

- It groups assets by function and not geography. This facilitates a meaningful and productive criticality analysis by focusing on function and the interrelationships of the systems to one another, and takes the physical complex design of modern plants into account.

- It quickly focuses attention on critical systems and the assets within them that affect the overall goals of the operation.

- It standardizes an approach that can be implemented at other facilities, especially those with similar equipment and design. This is especially valuable for organizations with multiple facilities.

The ignition system in your family minivan is a great example of a functional system. It has assets that belong to it, like the spark plugs, wires, coils (depending on age of car), computer modules for timing, and of course the power source. These 'assets' are the children of the parent ignition system. The ignition system, transmission, engine, cooling system, and others are part of a larger parent that could be termed the power train, separate from and at the same hierarchy 'level' as the cabin system, suspension and wheels, climate control, the corrosion control system (paint). Collectively they make the car, the whole.
In this case we have 4 levels:
- Car
  - Power Train
    - Ignition System
      - Spark Plugs
      - Wires
      - Timing Module
      - Battery

Functional System Approach to Criticality Analysis

Once you have your assets organized into a functional system-based hierarchy you will be able to approach your criticality analysis in a much more efficient way.

You may be familiar with a traditional RCM-style criticality analysis that starts and focuses at the asset level. If an asset fails in a number of particular ways (failure modes), what is the impact on its ability to do what it is supposed to do, and what is the result on its functionality? With an additional step one might ask what the effect is on the neighboring assets, but the focus is generally the asset itself. To gain an overall perspective on what the most critical assets are in the plant one would need to do this on every asset in the plant: a very time intensive and costly exercise. This gets very difficult when evaluating every pipe section, valve, sensor and so on.

There is a better way.

Using a functional system based hierarchy you can approach the criticality analysis from the top down and quickly zero in on your most critical assets. The first level of analysis starts by comparing functional systems to determine which ones have the biggest impact on the goals or mission of the facility. As critical systems are identified, the analysis then moves in focus to the next level of assets in those systems. Non-critical systems are either excluded from further analysis or deferred to later.

So how does one compare the functional systems against one another? How does one evaluate them for failure? Are there nuances that are different when looking at functional systems rather than individual assets? Systems don't have failure modes as defined in RCM. So how do you evaluate them?

Failure Scenarios versus Failure Modes

When starting a criticality analysis at the functional system level rather than the asset level we move from evaluating failure modes to evaluating failure scenarios.

A failure mode at the asset level is commonly described as the way an asset fails, such as rotating equipment that can experience a bearing failure. Even more specifically, it can experience bearing wear, bearing corrosion, or warping. This then focuses the attention to the net effect on the rotation and the consequence

A failure type is a description of a generic loss of function.
A chemical feed system suffers a loss of pumping.

A failure scenario describes the circumstances or event around a loss of function.
Loss of pumps resulting in high turbidity and blinded filters.

A failure mode looks at the specific ways an asset can fail.
A pump can have a bearing failure due to corrosion, wear or warping.

of such at the asset performance level. When there are multiple similar assets available, such as a bank of pumps, the results for each would be the same but the aggregate impact is often not considered, nor the overall affect on adjacent systems or the plant as a whole.

In contrast, a failure scenario at the system level takes a much wider and outward view of the net effect and the impact on overall objectives.

A failure scenario is comprised of two parts:

- A failure type, describing a generic yet fundamental loss of system functionality like a loss of pumping

- A description of specific and legitimate events or circumstances surrounding the generic loss of functionality

Failure Type: Generic Loss of System Functionality

As an example, if we examine a pumping system, it can fail to deliver its purpose in a few fundamental ways such as:

- A loss of pumping
- A loss of containment of the tank, piping, or valves (with a rupture or leak)
- A loss of valve functionality (stuck open or closed or incorrect position)
- A loss of control system functionality (loss of power, loss of signal, incorrect signal)
- A blockage

These generic functional descriptions or failure types are a good start and are common across almost any facility and any type of pumping system. These can be adjusted or added to according to local plant design. Keeping the failure types generic makes them useful across multiple designs and plants and permits comparisons across the plant as well as plant to plant.

Specific Circumstances

How these losses of functionality occur depends on the local context. This requires a description of plausible events or occurrences based on history. It is this specific description that reflects the local context and that takes into account the interrelationship between systems, the designs used, the types of assets and the materials of construction.

The description needs to be specific and relevant to the existing hardware.

For example, we all recognize that a fire in a control panel in the main breaker room will be very bad. However, if there were to be a fire, what would be the worst-case scenario? What if the fire happened during the weekend or at night? In which control panel could a fire affect the largest or the most sensitive parts of the plant?

Similarly, if a pumping system were to fail would it be worse if the pumps stopped due to a power failure, or due to a breach below the pressure loss detection limit, resulting in a sustained undetected discharge?

Describe the failure specifically so that it can be evaluated against the categories to find the worst consequences of failure. Ask this question: **What is the 3am call you do not want to get?** Keep it plausible and probable. Our guiding rule is: "No earthquakes, asteroids or aliens. Except in California (aliens, that is)." Yes, an asteroid crashing into earth would be a high impact and severe event – but it's not probable.

(Examples of both failure types and failure scenarios at the end of this chapter.)

Remember that this is different than a root cause analysis. We are not investigating why something failed but describing a potential failure and identifying the probable consequences.

Failure Scenarios and Evaluation Categories

Once the failure scenarios are determined for the types of systems, each functional system is evaluated using relevant and specific failure scenarios, against the categories previously determined as relevant to the overall goals. What is the impact of a failure like a particular loss of pumping on safety, on compliance, on capacity, on contractual obligations? Similarly, what impact does a loss of containment have? The impact will be described according to the defined levels of severity.

The severity and likelihood of the consequences to those criteria are evaluated largely based on historical data, including near misses. What we are looking for is the greatest impact and probability of occurrence. Often, several system failure scenarios are evaluated, and the "worst one(s)" picked for inclusion in the analysis and ranked in order of risk ranking. In comparing multiple scenarios you will compare multiple severities in multiple categories with different probabilities. You will need some tools to be able to do this – more on this in the next chapter.

Notice that we are concerned with a realistic system failure scenario and its effects rather than a specific gasket-by-gasket, or valve-by-valve, evaluation. What is the effect of leaking/discharging oil or raw sewage, for example, into the environment? Can the breach be detected before too long? Can it be effectively and quickly mitigated?

Once the risk ranking of a functional system is determined, the layout, local design, interconnected systems can be further evaluated through other tools like an FMEA. This is normally reserved for the top ranked 20% of the systems.

Moving from Functional Systems to Assets

Assets in a functional system will have the same criticality ranking as the system to which they belong or lower, but never higher. If a system has a ranking somewhere in the middle, then the default condition is that all assets in that system will also be ranked in the middle, at worst, possibly less, depending on the asset's contribution to the system functionality.

In this way one can very quickly determine where highly ranked or critical assets are because they will be in the highly ranked systems. The converse is also true, the systems with lesser ranking, will only have assets that will be lesser ranked as well.

If a low ranked system fails, which is deemed not to impact the overall objective much at all, then any asset inside that system that fails will never have a consequence worse than the system failure.

At this point a determination can be undertaken at the asset level as to which ones in the system of interest will cause the system to fail to deliver its stated objective, its functional purpose, and which assets will have little effect on the system functionality. The assets with little or no impact will be demoted in rank. Thus, critical assets are rapidly identified and their ranking set already.

The best analyses will provide a relative rank of all systems. Generally, the breakout for all the functional systems compared is 20% are ranked critical, 40% somewhat important, and the balance as not that important. The final list of critical assets will be smaller because not all the assets in a critical system will be equally important.

Key Advantages of a Functional System Approach

There are two key advantages to this approach over a traditional RCM approach to criticality analysis: efficiency and scope.

The functional system approach is much faster at determining which groups of assets affect the overall goals the most. This results in huge savings of time and resources. A criticality analysis done this way is normally completed in about 20% of the time it takes to complete an asset-by-asset exercise. In our experience it takes about 100 hours to do a system level analysis, in contrast to months for an asset-by-asset approach.

The functional system approach is outward looking to the other systems and overall facility with a view to maintenance activities and system risk identification. Conversely, an asset-by-asset FMEA or FMECA is intended to focus at the asset level with a view to reliability and redesign of the asset rather than an overall facility objective approach.

With the functional system approach we now have a plant wide, system by system ranking, as well as a list of the critical assets within the critical systems that pose the greatest risk to the overall objectives. Critical systems get our attention first for condition assessments and other activities. As time and budget permits, we can expand the analysis to go down the list.

All this in a fraction of the time a conventional asset-by-asset evaluation would take. By focusing on the critical systems, and setting aside the non-critical systems, we eliminate a huge amount of effort and cost, while validating and documenting our decisions instead of relying on educated best guesses.

The efficiency of the functional system approach is especially valuable for securing the support and sponsorship of executive and senior leadership. A major objective of any analysis is return on investment. Given the same return, minimizing the expense and investment improves that return.

The functional system failure scenario approach is rapid, accurate, and captures those factors that are of interest to senior management, as outlined before, and will be attractive. It is good stewardship of resources and the likelihood of support will be increased if the results achieved efficiently demonstrated a sharpened focus of limited resources to those areas that put the corporate objectives at risk.

Summary

There are several key elements to an effective criticality analysis, which need to be understood and in place prior to starting:

1. **Leadership** support and participation
2. Clear understanding of **facility mission objectives**
3. Well-defined criteria for evaluating criticality
4. Well-organized **asset hierarchy**
5. Starting from a **system-level approach**

With these foundational elements in place you are almost ready to start. Next, we look at the nuts and bolts of preparing for your analysis.

Table 4.1 is a sample of some typical Failure Types for some typical systems found at a municipal plant.

Table 4.1 - Sample Typical Municipal Wastewater Plant	
Example System	**Typical Failure Type**
Aeration	Blockage (gates) Loss of recirculation Tank degradation Tank/Channel loss of containment
Buildings	Accessibility malfunction (entry, stairs, egress) Environmental containment (roof, windows, doors) Electrical malfunction (lighting) Plumbing malfunction Structural malfunction
Blower Air	Blockage Diffuser malfunction Loss of blowing Loss of filtration Loss of containment Mechanical malfunction
Chemical Storage and Feed	Blockage Chemical quality Loss of delivery Loss of pumping Loss of containment
Clarifying	Blockage Drive malfunction Loss of containment Mechanical jamming Surface hydraulic malfunction Tank degradation
Compressed Air/Gas	Blockage Excess moisture Loss of filtration Loss of compressing Loss of containment
Electrical	Quality (phase, also drive quantity) Electrical fire Loss of continuity Short/ground

Example System	Typical Failure Type
Filtration	Controls malfunction Line blockage Loss containment Media/retention element blockage Media/retention element bypass
Instrumentation / Control	Loss of communication Incorrect communication Controls malfunction Incorrect signal/response Loss of signal/response
Pumping	Blockage Controls malfunction Loss of Containment Loss of pumping Mechanical jamming
Well	Blockage Blinding Casing Degradation Mechanical Loss of Pumping Loss of containment Water Level Water quality

Table 4.2 lists sampling of specific Failure Types for some example systems and their associated Scenario Details.

Table 4.2

System	Failure	Scenario Detail
Aeration System	Loss of pumping	Recirculation pump failure results in loss of ML return.
Aeration System	Rupture	Loss of union or break in header/grid piping results in loss of aeration grid and requirement to shut down aeration unit (during storm flow).

System	Failure	Scenario Detail
Backwash System	Controls malfunction	Loss of controls requires manual backwash procedures.
Chemical System	Chemical quality	Bad batch of neat polymer resulting in blockage of tank and lines.
Chemical System	Loss of pumping	Loss of two or more pumps potentially resulting in high turbidity and blinded filters.
Dewatering Station	Loss of pumping	Break of screw in conveyor results in loss of one filter press train until repaired.
Filter Pumping Station	Loss of pumping	Requirement to shut down pump station temporarily due to pump failure or discharge line failure results in bypassing filtrate equalization and shut down of filter presses.
Main Pump Station	Blockage	Blockage is not a practical scenario on the suction or discharge side
Main Pump Station	Loss of containment	Force main rupture in the pipe gallery
Pump Station	Controls malfunction	That disables all normal pumping functionality (there would have to be cascade of failures for this to occur). Assuming the override probes are still functional.
Pumping Station	Mechanical jamming	Jamming of impeller results in pump stoppage.
Settling System	Drive malfunction	Loss of sludge collection drive results in accumulation of solids on bottom of tank.

5

Preparing for a Criticality Analysis

The success of a criticality analysis depends on planning and preparation. Gathering the right information, getting the right tools, inviting the right people and so forth, will go a long way to getting the right results. Be sure to allocate sufficient preparation time to have all these elements ready before you start.

- Budget
- Required Information
- Participants
- Software Tools
- Working with a facilitator
- Setting a schedule

Budget

As you start organizing your resources and materials for the criticality analysis, you will begin to get a sense of your costs for putting together a budget. It is likely that you will need a preliminary budget in order to gain senior management approval for the analysis. This checklist will help you identify the resources you will need in terms of staff time, how many staff, their fully burdened cost, and the other resources mentioned below, including preparation time to gather the historical background, technical documentation, drawings, etc. Be sure to include a projected overall duration because while staff is participating in a criticality analysis they are not doing their regular job.

Required Information

Facility Goals & Objectives
You need a meaningful, clear and concise statement of corporate mission and facility objectives from senior management. Without this your analysis will miss its intended purpose.

Evaluation Categories
As discussed in the previous chapter, the evaluation categories define the scope and boundaries of the study, and determine the nature of the response and overall value of the study to the organization.

If the evaluation categories are too narrow, the analysis will become myopic and you forego a lot of potential value.

Evaluation categories that are too inclusive or expansive will bog the study down and can undermine the commitment made by management to allocate resources. At minimum you need three categories: safety, production and environmental. It's preferable to have five, up to eight. We've rarely worked with more than seven categories.

Remember that each category must directly relate to a mission or objective of the facility to be analyzed.

Asset Registry and Hierarchy
Make sure that your asset registry is complete and has been organized into a meaningful hierarchy prior to starting your analysis (see Chapter 4.) This will likely take some time to accomplish and will need to be considered in scheduling the analysis. Incomplete asset registries and disorganized hierarchies are the biggest roadblocks we encounter to completing an analysis.

There are cases where the asset register and hierarchy do not originate from the CMMS system. In an instance like this you will need asset IDs and types from your CMMS to coordinate with your hierarchy. In order for the results to influence the work order process, the criticality analysis must relate to the asset IDs in the CMMS.

Additional Technical Information
You will also need some official drawings of the plant, process & instrumentation diagrams (P&IDs) or at minimum process flow diagrams (PFDs), as well as complete an operations and maintenance history of the plant as possible, including knowl-

edge of failures and mishaps. There may be good documentation of this history but it more likely resides with the experts you will invite to the analysis. Note, that when reviewing the history any "near misses" should be treated as actual events. Current safety thinking and methodology counts near misses the same as actual events.

Participants

Getting the right participants in the room is vital to the ultimate value of your criticality analysis.

Experts from operations, maintenance, engineering, and electrical are always important. Representation from additional areas will be driven by the evaluation categories you determined to be relevant to your mission and objectives. If environmental, health and safety is to be included in a significant way, then an EH&S person should be included in the list. When commercial terms or contractual issues arise you will want to be able to consult the business center leadership.

All participants should be leaders at the facility with substantial experience and oversight, to bring credibility and historical context to the analysis. An additional benefit to the criticality analysis is that it will serve as means of documenting and preserving the institutional knowledge and expertise currently held by these professionals. It will also align all the groups to the real priorities that emerge from the analysis, and help sideline pet projects.

Software Tools

A criticality analysis is not a trivial exercise. It also does not need to be an overwhelming effort. The right tools will help you keep it manageable. Yes, it is possible to conduct a criticality analysis with pen and paper – but why would you when there are good tools available? Some kind of software will be necessary to record, calculate, and analyze, and to be consistent. You can use:

- Home-made Excel spreadsheets
- Simple third party spreadsheets
- Modules in EAMs when they exist
- Premier third party stand alone software tools specifically designed to maximize the results of the effort

Consider your needs when determining which tools to use. If you only have a simple plant with few systems, then it might be possible to set up your own Excel spreadsheet. With more complex facilities you will need more sophisticated tools. Look for these capabilities in the tools you choose:

- Intuitive and easy interface
- Configurable to your specific context and needs
- Develops and/or imports a hierarchy
- Flexible, with enough categories and weighting options
- Allows for multiple means of systems failure
- Allows for weighting of severity of failures
- Allows for weighting the numbers of failures
- Provides a relative ranking of all results
- Documents and captures follow-up items through the process
- Supports ISO55000 implementation
- Permits sensitivity analysis
- Provides multiple levels of user access
- Exports results in multiple formats
- Works with your current EAM or CMMS
- Supported over the long term

You will also need access to the CMMS as needed for verification of some event that arises in a discussion. You may want to include a CMMS expert on the analysis team.

Find a Facilitator

Few organizations have the internal resources to conduct these types of analyses on a regular basis. It is generally advisable to hire a trained and practiced facilitator for the first analysis, who can then train some of your staff to assume that role by the end. Subsequent analyses can then be led in-house.

It is important that the facilitator have strong industry knowledge of the facility to be analyzed. This would include not only the nature of the processes, equipment and assets used, but also the nature of the relevant evaluation categories applicable to the facility and considered important to the company.

The facilitator should also be very familiar with the hierarchy, preferably having had a hand in creating it.

Set a Schedule

If your team has never done a criticality analysis before, setting a schedule may seem like a bit of a black box. If your team has done an FMEA before, a functional system level criticality analysis will not be the same and will take less time. The total time required to complete an analysis will depend on multiple variables. An average analysis will take roughly 80 to 100 hours, spread over several weeks.
The schedule depends on several factors:

- Staff availability.
- Level of staff expertise available.
- Coordination with other programs currently under way or that would follow: condition assessment, capital planning, safety reviews, budget planning for the next fiscal, etc.
- Availability of the technical data for the facility.
- Readiness of the asset register and hierarchy. Until these are complete there is little point in starting.
- Availability of facilities to hold the meetings.

A criticality analysis can be tiring and drain staff ability to focus and participate meaningfully. Once sustained focus is no longer viable there is little point in continuing for the day. Usually it is best to limit sessions to no more than 4 hours, with no more than three sessions per week.

Summary

Someone once said if you fail to prepare, prepare to fail. Adequate preparation will set you up for a successful criticality analysis. Once you have collected your information, organized your resources and identified your team, you're ready to go! It's time to conduct your criticality analysis.

Conducting an Analysis

Here are the basic steps for conducting a criticality analysis. We have set this out as a checklist or task-list and described best practices where applicable. There are generally three phases to a criticality analysis:

Pre-Analysis Preparation
Phase 1: Setting the Parameters
Phase 2: Conducting the Analysis

Pre-Analysis

- Gain approval from management and agreement with the participating groups to hold a criticality analysis.
- Plan to hold sessions over several weeks or months on a periodic basis. This will usually be the case given operational priorities.
- Hire an experienced outside facilitator who is familiar with this type of analysis as well as the general issues associated with your type of facility, or designate an internal person who has experience with a criticality analysis.
- Schedule the event, a suitable conference room, and inform the participants. Make sure you have enough space and seats.
- Ensure you have access to the AV equipment you need and that it's reserved for each session. You will need a projector and screen, a computer that runs software to capture the progress and data, perhaps a sound system, and video and/or audio recording equipment. Recording the analysis is optional

but we have found it beneficial. Often a smartphone is sufficient for audio recording.
- Designate a team member who will be the scribe. Make sure they can familiarize themselves with the software to be used prior to starting the analysis.
- Preferably the day before, but at least on the day of the analysis, prep the room 30 minutes before the session is to begin. Try the software, connect the computer and try the projector and screen, test the sound system to make sure it's working, and test any recording device you might use.

The sessions will be divided into two main events. The first is setting the parameters of the analysis and making sure everyone understands the terms and focus and is on the same page. The second phase is the actual analysis.

Phase 1: Setting Parameters

Start well by starting on time. After introductions, review the agenda for the session, the participant expectations, the scheduled breaks, and the points of exit in case of emergency. While this is a serious exercise, an easy going but professional culture is often more productive than a rigid climate.

Introduce the overall process and review the elements of the analysis.

Asset Hierarchy

Review the hierarchy, as an overview only, reminding the participants that the review will be at the system level, and not the asset level.

Definitions

Review the definitions of a system versus an asset and clarify the objectives of the analysis – to discover what is essential. This is different from an FMEA or FMECA, which your participants may already be familiar with.

Evaluation Categories

Set up the categories that are to be evaluated. This would involve a good understanding of the mission statement of the organization, its values, and the stated goals of the facility to be evaluated. These categories can be set up in advance if desired. In that case just review them with the group.

Recall that the categories must reflect the corporate values and the objectives set for the facility and should be carefully selected because once the analysis starts, they should not be modified.

Definitions and Settings

ID	Active	Category	Cont
1	☑	Staff Safety	4
2	☑	Public Safety	4
3	☑	Enviromental	3
4	☑	Process Capacity	3
5	☑	Public Relations	1
6	☑	Operating Costs	2
7	☐	Category seven	1
8	☐	Category eight	1
9	☐	Category nine	1
10	☐	Category ten	1
11	☑	Probablity	1

Figure 5

Review and clarify what is specifically meant by each category. For example, do environmental consequences include or exclude the fines associated with them? When considering multiple facilities one or two categories might not apply given local context, regulations, or crossing state boundaries.

Ranking & Weighting Categories

Set the ranked importance of these categories relative to each other, reflective of mission and company values. As an example in the Categories graphic the relative weighting of Safety to Public Relations is 4:1.

Definitions of Severity

Create definitions for each level of severity. Recall that when defining levels of severity its important to keep in mind three facets:

- The overall level of the impact,
- The rapidity or speed the impact happens, and
- The ability to mitigate the impact or intervene.

Review what makes an event the worst level? What makes an event a catastrophe, something "never to happen" event? Conversely review what makes something a tolerable event, and everything in between.

Try to avoid hard numbers in a definition that are time or economy dependent.

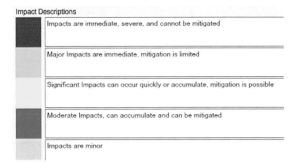

Impact Descriptions

	Impacts are immediate, severe, and cannot be mitigated
	Major Impacts are immediate, mitigation is limited
	Significant Impacts can occur quickly or accumulate, mitigation is possible
	Moderate Impacts, can accumulate and can be mitigated
	Impacts are minor

Figure 6

Relative Scale of Severity

If you are able to adjust the relative importance of each level of severity in your software, make the initial relative weighting between the levels as linear as possible. At a later time the relative weighting of one level to another can be adjusted to favor single serious event failures or to favor high-count lower severity failures.

Similarly so with the probability weighting: initially set it to unity, such that low or highly probable events are treated equally. Later you can set skew the probability weighting to be more sensitive to highly probable events.

Reminder!

A **failure type** is a description of a generic loss of function.
A chemical feed system suffers a loss of pumping.

A **failure scenario** describes the circumstances or event around a loss of function.
Loss of pumps resulting in high turbidity and blinded filters.

A **failure mode** looks at the specific ways an asset can fail.
A pump can have a bearing failure due to corrosion, wear or warping.

Introduce Failure Scenarios

Remember when developing and considering various failure scenarios, the probability or plausibility of the scenario is important. You are trying to reflect reality, and thus real criticality. Asteroid impact is of course the worst-case scenario, with tremendous destruction and no way to mitigate the effects on all fronts but it's not a likely event for your facility.

Similarly so for aliens and earthquakes. Although in the coastal areas of California, this is actually a real consideration (the UFO part). We encourage only plausible and historic events, including near misses. A near miss is an event, that almost occurred, and would have occurred had there not been intervention, or 'luck'. Next time there might not be interventions or warning. Treat near misses as events. You just got lucky that time.

Phase 2: Begin the Criticality Analysis

Together with the company sponsor the facilitator should organize the progress through the analysis to cover mechanical systems first, with the electrical and SCADA systems in a block at some later date. The electrical team member(s) do not need to be present for the major mechanical analysis. This may not be the case for the mechanical staff as the failure of the electrical system often impacts mechanical areas, especially related to access and staff safety. Usually operations and maintenance will be participating 100% of the time, with electrical having less scheduled involvement.

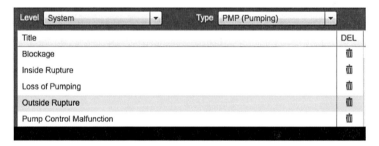

Figure 7

Start with something obvious and easy. In most cases this is a pump system. There is something intrinsically understandable about pumping systems. They either work or they don't, they are not too complex, and basically involve moving something from A to B. As you get more familiar with the definitions and the process begin to tackle more complex systems that are more difficult to understand.

- Review the systems identified in the hierarchy and pick a simple pump system.

Questions, Questions, Questions!

The art of effective facilitation lies in asking lots of good questions.

During the failure scenario discussion, or discovery phase, the recollection of events or near misses might be hazy. A great way to jog memories is to ask questions about possible occurrences from your own experience: "Has this ever happened?" or "I recall at one site …"

The past is sometimes recalled far more simply than it actually was. Significant events might be dismissed as unimportant and not brought up for discussion. So asking good questions with plenty of examples not only helps recall, but also prompts recognition of significant events and their relevance to the current discussion.

- Review the assets in that system, noting what the system contains.
- Review the failure types of a pump system. The list of failure types can be pre-set by the consultant or a separate time before the session can be set up to generate this list. A thorough understanding of system failure types, distinct from asset failure modes is needed to generate the list.
- Using the general list of system failure types, develop some initial specific failure scenarios, much like we described earlier. (A sample list of both failure types and scenarios is listed at the end of the Chapter 4.)
- As you start with a failure type, such as loss of pumping, ask under what real life scenario can the pump station, for example, lose pumping?
- Remind everyone of the need for specific scenarios for each failure type, even providing sample examples from another facility or earlier analysis.
- Remind the team of the major rules: no earthquakes (unless in such an area), asteroids, or aliens.
- Refine the answer by asking for the worst way this can happen, based on realistic expectations and history of this facility, or even facilities to prompt thinking.
- Capture the scenario in the software, and begin to set the level of severity for each category, as well as the probability, of the event happening.
- Remind the team at this point that it is not a condition assessment, and that the scenario is based on the history of occurrence and near misses, on design, selection of materials, interrelationship with other systems affecting it, local context (environment), suitability of access and detection, and NOT on the condition of the assets or system. Remind the team of this every time it comes up (because it will).
- Capture as many scenarios as needed to be sure the worst case has been identified. Here is a sample of 3 scenarios for the pump station showing the failure type, the specific scenario under which the failure type exists, and the resulting consequences if failure occurs.
- The next step is to composite the individual scenarios into one summarized scenario. This process will simplify your calculations a bit if you are doing this in a spreadsheet.

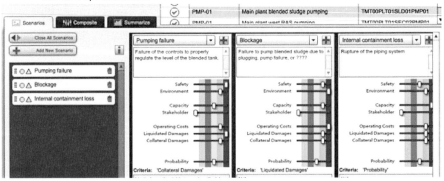

Figure 8

- Summarize the major scenario or two that pose the worst case.
- Remember also to capture the follow-up items as they are presented in the discussions of each scenario. This should happen often. However, don't allow the process to be derailed by solving follow-up items. You will probably need to remind the team that identified follow-up items are for later attention.
- Once all the information is captured for the pumping system, move onto the next system. Continue through the same process until all systems have been analyzed.

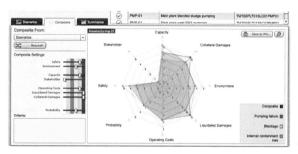

Figure 9

Additional Notes

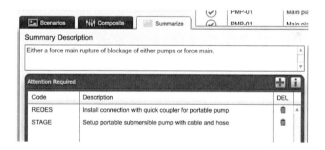

Figure 10

Leadership

Picking a good facilitator is important. Facilitating a session requires not only familiarity with the process, but also field experience, or some association with the field experience.

Leadership needs a certain enthusiasm or dynamism, not only to draw out reluctant participants, perhaps due to skepticism, general shyness, or lack of familiarity. The leadership and facilitator must be able to temper and steer the dominant and strong personalities so as not to bias the process and results, and encourage the less vocal to speak up. This is actually an aspect of managing the room and the process. The process is designed to elicit actual risk areas, not validate pet projects.

Leaders must also recognize that this is not intended to be a solution session. Yes, issues and follow-up items are intended to be captured, but for follow-up, not as a session to solve every issue that is discovered or captured.

Remember the Basic Rules

Good leader also reviews the basic rules every so often and keeps everyone on track. There is a tendency to stray a little each time discussion moves into technical details that tend to interest the participants. They can stray into solution finding mode, forget the levels of severity and what they mean, or the concepts of looking at failure scenarios rather than failure modes, or get distracted by questions about asset condition.

Doughnuts

An army runs on food. Bring doughnuts or provide lunch. The team will appreciate the break; it will fuel their brains and engender a general feeling of being appreciated. This is an important analysis, and the privilege and responsibility of involvement should be rewarded, even if only symbolically. If doughnuts are taboo and more healthy fare is desired then make that adjustment. But I've never seen doughnuts snubbed.

And don't forget the coffee, with real cream. This facilitator likes real cream.

Summary

Although it takes time, the actual criticality analysis is a fairly straightforward process. Adequate preparation is very important, especially in preparing the hierarchy. We also see the best success when sufficient care is taken to define terms and make sure everyone is on the same page before diving right in to the analysis. With a successful analysis completed, you can move to the next phase of applying the results and realizing the benefits.

Section 3

Next Steps

Applying the Results

When you have completed your criticality analysis you will have a ranked list of critical assets as well as a list of follow-up items that were identified through the process. Now you will put a plan in place to address the items requiring immediate attention and you will start applying the results of the analysis to targeting and prioritizing the rest of your AM activities.

Reviewing the ranked list, highly critical systems and assets should be addressed first. There are many tools of a sound asset management program that can be applied: maintenance optimization, condition assessments, refurbishment planning, capital planning, additional analyses like an FMEA or FMECA to zero in deeper at the asset and sub-asset level. Some will be done in parallel, some sequentially, often the results looping back and refining one of the other exercises. Where you start will depend on your local context, but there are some things that are easier than others. Generally, a good place to start is with the lowest hanging fruit, or easiest to execute follow-up items.

Review the follow-up list and identify the simple items that influence the risk ranking in the top 20% of the list. Things that can be easily implemented with little or

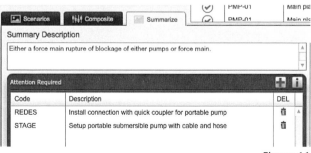

Figure 11

no budget expenditure, that involve some change in procedure and monitoring are easily started.

Other items that fall within the confines of one of the other AM tools listed above will require more effort. Then there will be more difficult follow-up items that might involve other departments, IT, operations, administration, EH&S, HR, engineering, purchasing, or some combination.

In parallel with the follow-up list, the next three that should be started are an FMEA to identify key failure modes of the critical assets; condition assessments on the critical systems and assets; and a PMO initiative.

FMEA

Results from the FMEA will tell you which assets in a system are the ones that can upset the system functionality the most. These are THE critical assets within a system and will be the first focal point of revisiting maintenance and monitoring programs based on the key failure modes of the assets identified by the FMEA.

The study might also suggest material changes and/or design changes in an asset like a different shaft material or shaft style, as example, which has greater reliability. An FMEA may be a long-term exercise and will likely involve not only engineering, but also procurement.

Condition Assessments

A condition assessment can be a large undertaking, but it's also necessary to know the condition of critical assets. A targeted expenditure in this area to the critical systems and assets is not only wise but also important as it can significantly influence so many other asset management facets like PMO, capital planning and design adjustment, and reduce risk of an unwanted event.

As the condition assessment data is assembled on the most critical items first, maintenance plans and activities can be targeted to the highest priority items.

If a critical system is in good shape, then at minimum the FMEA inspired monitoring program should continue, as should the optimized maintenance program discussed next. If the system is in poor condition then decisions must be made regarding refurbishment or replacement, and these impact capital planning.

Work Order Management

Much of this effort impacts and leads to a work order optimization, which is actually a reflection of a maintenance optimization: to stop doing the things that don't matter; to start doing the things that make a difference; and to keep doing the things that are making a difference.

Maintenance Myth:
If it ain't broke, fix it anyway.

Sometimes the assumption is made that a critical asset must be the subject of aggressive preventive maintenance, whether it needs it or not. In fact, a critical asset may just need monitoring or critical spares to be stored.

Fixing something that doesn't need fixing actually increases the likelihood that it will fail. Criticality ranking determines how much attention a system or asset gets, not whether it needs fixing. Determining if an asset should be fixed depends on if it has 'failed', and what constitutes 'failure' must be defined.

For example, a critical pump might be running smoothly, with nothing out of spec. But the pump efficiency might be declining little by little. Its criticality determines that we pay a lot of appropriate attention to it. But we don't need to fix anything until it performs in such a way that it has failed. In the case of a pump, failure could be operating below a certain percentage of efficiency. It is a poor maintenance plan that as a matter of routine rebuilds pumps every 6 months whether they need it or not, in the name of preventive maintenance.

Are you fixing things that aren't broken? Criticality does not necessarily mean fix it; it means pay attention.

In simple terms, the systems posing the greatest risk begin to drive where to apply greatest attention.

- How can the critical items fail?
- In what condition are they and are they already failing?
- What gets monitored to capture that failure, and how do we best maintain it?

Capital Planning

The criticality analysis will also guide the capital planning program to focus on more vulnerable and critical areas of the operations, influenced by the condition assessment results; and focus less on the unimportant areas, regardless of condition. The criticality rankings combined with condition assessments will direct where to spend money first, especially if money is in limited supply. And it usually is.

It is important to note that if the follow-up items change the system design, then the system should be re-evaluated and the new ranking incorporated. This will result, or should, in a re-ordered risk ranking of the systems, and over time will tell a chronological narrative of the overall facility, with commensurate risk reduction.

Summary

Applying the results of your criticality analysis will help direct the next steps of your asset management and reliability programs. You will be able to target your resources toward the systems and assets that need the most attention. As improvements are made to processes and design, your criticality rankings will be influenced. Next we look at keeping your criticality analysis up to date and expanding it across your organization.

Criticality Going Forward

Criticality Analysis Across Multiple Facilities

If your organization has more than one facility, it is prudent to complete a criticality analysis in one facility, and then roll out the program across the other facilities.

Generally the best approach is to start with the facility that is most representative of the rest. This facility will have the greatest variety of systems and equipment represented at the majority of plants. The set up of system types and asset types at the initial site will lay the foundation for the organization and structure of the hierarchy as a whole. As you move to another facility there will be some modifications of the asset register and hierarchy but the bulk of the work will already be done. This allows for a much more efficient implementation of criticality analyses across your organization.

Identical designs and systems across facilities have the advantage of making the initial set up more efficient, and then the analysis more efficient. However, it is still necessary to conduct a unique analysis for each location. Be mindful of variations in design or materials selected, of different upstream and downstream systems, of changes in size, changes in context, and changes in state or regional regulations.

We don't advocate that identical systems be identically ranked across all facilities. Each system should be re-evaluated at the other facilities for a more certain analysis result. There are always local context nuances that come into play, and some are significant and more complicated.

Keeping Your Criticality Analysis Updated

It is important to regularly review your criticality rankings and mission parameters and update any changes.

Asset criticality is relatively constant, in contrast to asset condition, which can change from day to day and even minute to minute and requires careful monitoring. You could be tempted to "set it and forget it" once you have completed your criticality analysis. However, this will ignore fundamental changes in design or upgrades, in mission objectives, changes in regulation (including permits), changes in sensitivity to safety or environmental issues, economic downturn, commodity prices, commercial terms and contractual terms, and even in some cases SOP and security policy rules.

Criticality depends on design, system interactions, and objectives. As critical systems are addressed per the follow-up items, improvements, or redesign, they will have their potential consequences of failure altered, and hence the risk ranking changed.

It is good practice to revisit the criticality analysis on a schedule that reflects the rate at which the systems and assets in those systems are changed or modified. As a start, an annual review is suggested. This can be adjusted over time to find the appropriate frequency. Alternatively, revisiting and re-evaluating a critical system after it has been altered can also suffice, and makes the overall results more dynamic than a yearly snapshot.

Fortunately, reviewing and updating criticality is far more efficient and accomplished in far less time than the initial analysis. Subsequent evaluations are not as involved and can usually be accomplished in a half-day session.

This is where third-party software is beneficial as it can provide a durable and consistent platform across time and facilities, with unique and effective ways of representing the results, without the need to rely on internal staff to support it over the long term. Good software will also provide participants with details of historic evaluations and data as a starting point to refresh memories and re-calibrate their thinking.

As systems and assets are improved or redesigned, your updated criticality analysis will rank new systems at the top for priority action. With time, a story begins to unfold of risk mitigation and an overall facility profile that is improving.

This story, with the documentation to back it up, validates that your program is delivering value and will help you pursue additional benefits and reliability leadership initiatives.

Realizing the Benefits

Financial Benefits

There are significant benefits that follow completing your criticality analysis:

- Short-term and mid-term maintenance and reliability gains
- Decision support for effective and efficient capital planning
- Improved safety that could save someone's life
- Focus for managing and reducing overall operations risk
- Improved financial results through increased up time and greater reliability

The results of your analysis can also be applied in two areas that are often overlooked:

- Insurance
- Reserves

The premiums that organizations pay for insurance coverage depend on inherent risk as assessed by the insurer, who needs enough detail to accurately model the risk. Insufficient information drives up the premiums, to cover unidentified risk, as does an inherently risky operation.

Organizations also carry reserves on their books to cover the deductibles on their insurance policies.

The information gathered through an effective criticality analysis can be used in a variety of ways to lower premiums and reserves, and ultimately, improve the bottom line.

1. The criticality analysis improves an organization's understanding of its inherent risks. This increased granularity of understanding can assist underwriters in more accurately modeling your operations. More data means less guessing, which means less contingency included in the calculations, so the numbers are less inflated: less extra money is required to cover the unknown. This should result in reduced premiums.

2. A better understanding of your risk profile helps you address areas of risk, even in the short term. This ability to identify, address, and reduce short-term risk demonstrates a firm grasp on the business and risk, raises the insurer's confidence and can further influence the premiums.

3. Regular and long-term actions to deal with the higher risk items demonstrate an organization's continual improvement process and increasing ability to manage risk, again reducing the long-term risk profile. This will further aid in premium reduction over time, all of which is a net benefit to the bottom line.

4. It is possible to balance the potential premium savings against the ability to reduce the reserves on the books, the money set aside for the deductible, or even self-insurance. Some organizations might elect to take an immediate benefit to the bottom line and reduce the required reserves, and leave the cash flow expense allocated for premiums unchanged. Some might elect for a combination of both reserve and premium reduction, others might elect to take on additional insurance or shift the policy coverage based on lesser need in one area.

There are, of course, several areas of insurance that can be affected by an increased understanding of and active steps to reduce any risk. Some of these are environmental, third party, and workers' compensation insurance. If a strong focus on safety is included in the analysis, then even workers' compensation premiums can be positively affected, which can translate to large sums of money saved since workers' compensation claims and insurances are significant liabilities.

The potential to reduce pressure on cash flow and reserves through better identified and mitigated risk is very good news for the financial leaders of any organization. Be sure to communicate this potential value to your risk management and financial departments.

Communication: Telling the Story

Communication is key to getting things done. To be heard, we need to be sure to speak in a language that our intended audience understands. You will need to translate the technical "speak" of the criticality analysis into terms that senior managers with financial obligations value.

You need to communicate the technical and operational benefits of the analysis and show the value of next steps to the bottom line. These managers can support and sustain your efforts, but they can also say no and stand in the way. This is rarely motivated by a desire to be obstructionist. Instead, they need to understand that the focus of what you do and the financial benefit to the organization.

You will need to show the value in real numbers. Don't just say it's "good to do" or say it will "help financially". It will likely be advantageous to collaborate with team members from other departments who can help translate and quantify the benefits. Enlist the help of those who see the long-term financial benefit, the improved health of the business, the improved EH&S security of staff, and the long-term improved bottom line.

When you are telling the story to management, either to enlist support for a criticality analysis or to share the results, it is important is to be able to connect the dots from focused action and revised management focus to the financial benefit. Be sure to show:

- The new focus on critical systems
- What actions will you take and what actions will be discontinued
- Where and how will spending change and for how long
- Expected cost reductions and how they are verifiable
- Expected safety improvements and risk reductions

It's important to show the change in financial and resource commitment before and after the study and which risks will be addressed and reduced. Try to monetize the change in risk if you can. This might not be easy when dealing with safety issues but the risk management department in your organization can assist you with cost of accidents to the company, and any past examples of improvements.

Remember that this goes way beyond just reduced hospital bills and health insurance premiums. The financial impact includes reserves for litigation, liability insurance, workers' compensation, lost time productivity, OT to make up the staffing shortfall and so on. It can get rather complicated, so get help. Getting buy-in from those who can help monetize this is a good way to work on the message that gets communicated up the chain to senior management.

Above all, remember integrity. Don't use smoke and mirrors to try to get something you need; others will see through it.

A Final Note on Criticality and Reliability Leadership

As a reliability leader you are working to help your team and organization achieve its aim and deliver value.

As a leader in criticality analysis, you will set the direction, help make it happen, guide the discussion and help others do their part, all while keeping your eye on the goal of delivering a meaningful and useful criticality analysis that will aid in wise and efficient use of resources.

All of this works toward the ultimate goal of bringing value to the bottom line, holistically, economically, environmentally, and socially.

Lead with integrity. Do the right things, for the right reasons, in the right order, and you will get the right results.

Appendix 1: Criticality Analysis and ISO Standards

The ISO55000 Standards set out to define a framework of core elements and systems for successful asset management. Building on the main themes of BSI PAS55, ISO55000 expands its view to a broader understanding of what delivering asset management really means.

An effective criticality analysis will support many of the core values and themes of ISO55000. A criticality analysis will also assist in satisfying some of the requirements prescribed for asset management systems.

Delivering Value

The overarching focus of ISO55000 is on the value an asset provides to an organization, which can be tangible or intangible, financial or non-financial. A criticality analysis is inevitably focused on discovering the value of assets and their relative importance to meeting organizational objectives. The results of the analysis will then drive decision-making for deriving value from the assets.

Alignment of Objectives

One of the key values of the original PAS55 document was alignment of organizational objectives from the top down. ISO55000 takes that a step further to alignment of objectives for achieving maximum value from the assets. Many companies tend to operate in organizational silos with little sharing and coordination between engineering, maintenance, operations or finance, for example. An effective criticality analysis requires cross-functional collaboration through its process and will result in shared knowledge. There is tremendous value in this collaborative process and in the common data that everyone can use for decision support towards organizational objectives.

Transparent and Consistent Decision-Making

At the core of a criticality analysis is establishing solid, documented support for making the best decisions in balancing conflicting demands for resources between asset groups and between important but sometimes competing priorities like safety, environment, production and corporate social responsibility. The results of a criticality analysis deliver the decision support needed to meet the mandate for transparent and consistent decision-making.

Managing Organizational Risk

A criticality analysis is an important step in risk management. It identifies potential risk, allowing for mitigation, and then takes this knowledge of risk and applies it to setting priorities and decision-making focused on organizational objectives and outcomes.

Balance Between Short-Term Planning and Long-Term Needs

A criticality analysis will help identify immediate needs and actions for short-term business planning, at the same time as helping establish long-term lifecycle priorities.

Knowledge About Asset Base

A successful asset management culture will have strong asset knowledge at its core. A criticality analysis integrates, documents and preserves asset knowledge that may currently only reside within various organizational silos, as previously mentioned, or that may be held only by key individuals. As a criticality analysis is maintained this knowledge bank will grow and will be invaluable in supporting the rest of the asset management systems.

It should also be noted that a criticality analysis will be useful in satisfying some of the documentation and audit trail requirements for certification.

Clarity

Finally, as we noted in the preface, the biggest challenges facing organizations trying to implement an asset management system are **knowing where to start** and **setting priorities**. Organizations need clarity and direction on where they are headed and how to get to there.

"ISO55000 provides a structured view of what the organization is try to achieve and how to balance things like performance, environment, and safety to achieve organizational value," said Rhys Davies in the Dec/Jan 2014 issue of Uptime Magazine.

A criticality analysis supports and informs the ISO55000 structured view and is vital for setting priorities and providing cross-functional direction for achieving organizational value.

—

Appendix 2: Case Studies

The criticality analysis approach that we have outlined has been successfully used in a variety of complex facilities and systems. The analysis consistently identifies significant unrecognized risks as well as quantifying the potential dollar cost of these risks.

The following case studies in particular demonstrate three of the key elements of an effective criticality analysis discussed in this book:

- **The efficiency of a functional systems approach instead of a discrete asset focus**, allowing the analysis to be completed with less time and cost while delivering more meaningful results.
- **The importance of including 100 percent of systems and assets** to ensure identification of previously unrecognized critical assets and sub-components, often with surprising findings.
- **The value of flexibility to include evaluation categories important and unique to the client** resulting in an analysis truly reflective of the client's values and constraints.

The case studies presented here involve a ground water remediation site, a large municipal system, and an industrial water treatment system within a refinery. Each study had a unique set of evaluation categories determined by the client's values and the unique performance, contractual, and regulatory issues affecting the facilities. In each case study, the criticality analysis identified previously unknown significant system risks, allowing the client to take specific action to mitigate those risks. Due to confidentiality considerations, specific names and the actual numerical data have been removed.

Case One: Ground Water Remediation System

Situation

A major refining operation in southern California includes a ground water remediation process consisting of extraction wells, a fluidized bed activated-media treatment process with filtration, and internal re-use of the treated water. This groundwater treatment process is heavily regulated and closely monitored by state regulatory agencies. The system design incorporates a small amount of excess capacity to help meet the annual target but given the annual turnaround requirements each year there is very little room for down-time outside the refinery schedule, making up-time a key performance metric.

In mid 2004 a sequence of unusual, but not extraordinary, events led to an extended shutdown, jeopardizing the ability of the system to meet the annual treatment targets before the year was half over. This placed the owner at considerable risk for regulatory actions and fines.

Because the process is relatively robust and reliable, such a situation had not been anticipated even though excellent engineering and operational management had been in place. It became clear that conventional approaches through process reviews, HAZOPs, and an aggressive maintenance program, were not adequate and the need to find the true risks in the system was paramount.

Response

The owner's engineering staff worked to engineer out future occurrences of similar events. However, they quickly found that what caused the shutdown was mostly an odd combination of circumstances and otherwise quite random and normally inconsequential failures. **In short, they could not find what to fix.**

The owner requested assistance in the evaluation of the overall process to identify the as yet hidden risks and related potential issues in order to prevent future similar and unforeseen occurrences. A criticality analysis was commissioned where the owner's system experts including engineers and operators were brought together with a criticality analysis expert facilitator. Inclusion of 100% of the overall process units in this functional area of the refinery and inclusion of pipes and valves as a separate group asset proved essential. The registry comprised in excess of 30 main functional systems and in excess of 200 discrete main assets. Against this backdrop of a comprehensive asset registry, leveraging the functional systems approach rather than a discrete asset approach resulted in not only a more efficient process, but also more meaningful results.

Given the relatively limited scope of the system as compared to a plant wide analysis, a few hours of preparation and a day of workshops accomplished an analysis of the complete remediation system, and produced remarkable and surprising results.

Results

While the owner's focus was primarily on preventing recurrence of the recent event, a full analysis of the system revealed several key aspects that led to a more comprehensive understanding of the process and associated risks. Specific improvement opportunities were identified that would immensely reduce risk with remarkably little effort and expense. Some of these are:

Final Filter – In order to save time in the analysis, the client system experts initially suggested ignoring a treated water filter that had been merely an annoyance to them. The filter had been added to the process as an afterthought in order to treat minor and rare fluctuations in quality that had since been worked out. However, once analyzed, it was found that this filter posed the highest risk within the entire process. The owner representatives had been focusing on treatment capacity concerns, but thorough analysis revealed that an important spill/overflow requirement could easily be violated at high probability due to the filter. Simply addressing the failure modes or even removing the filter from service would increase reliability of the overall process immensely. Potential losses here could reach well into the hundreds of thousands of dollars (larger investigations, cleanup, local and State fines) at a fairly high degree of probability.

Fluidizing Recirculation – The central treatment aspect in the process is a biologically active media fluidized bed reactor. Analysis revealed that many potential failures throughout the process led to the consequence of loss of fluidizing flow in the reactor, leading to congealing of the bed, which in turn required its replacement at great cost and loss of production. It was recognized that the system could be quickly, easily, and cheaply modified to provide the capability to re-circulate fluidizing flow, which would prevent congealing the bed. This one simple change, consisting of adding a short length of pipe and a valve, eliminated or significantly reduced the consequences of numerous potential failures throughout the process and eliminated a majority of the risk associated with treatment capacity and the consent decree treatment limits. Failures to meet treatment limits are fined at over $1MM per day.

Level Controls – Sometime after the process was designed and installed, an equalization tank was added at the inlet into the process. Controls were included to operate the pumps to manage the level in the tank. However, the added functions of "equalization" and the associated components had not been sufficiently evaluated in respect to the overall process. Analysis revealed many potential failures that would result in the equalization tank either going dry or overflowing. To complicate matters, an overflow, while contained, would be considered equal to an actual environmental discharge, and thus deemed unacceptable by the client (see next item). There were no backup or failure controls such as high and low alarms and interlocks installed in the tank and integrated into the process controls. Adding these simple controls would eliminate a large number of potential failures and significantly reduce overall system risk. Costs associated with these events range from a few thousand to tens of thousands of dollars (investigations and crew lost time).

Containment – The analysis revealed that treatment capacity, which had been the complete focus of the owner, was not the only regulatory requirement that applied or was at risk. In fact, the severity of spilling untreated or partially treated groundwater was at least as high, if not higher, than treatment capacity objectives. Analysis revealed the majority of potential failures resulted in spills and overflows, violating this regulatory requirement. When the facility was constructed, an area with a simple six-inch concrete berm was used for containment. Existence of the berm was assumed to be adequate for containment. However, analysis revealed that numerous potential failures could lead to overflow of containment. By raising the berm and extending it to include the entire process, the majority of these potential failures would be eliminated or their consequences significantly reduced. Potential losses here could reach well into the hundreds of thousands of dollars (larger investigations, cleanup, local and State fines).

Summary
The criticality analysis identified the issues behind the original major occurrence and uncovered numerous other risks. Through the analysis simple and cost effective solutions were identified, which immensely reduced the risk profile for the entire process in all risk areas. Further, what was thought to be an inconspicuous and apparently insignificant process component was actually of major importance. Conventional analysis and evaluation of what had happened failed to reveal meaningful ways to address the situation and prevent recurrence in the future. The investment effort and cost to perform criticality analysis were insignificant in comparison to the value gained.

Case Two: Public Utility, Pacific Northwest

Situation
A public works department of a major American city decided to begin an infrastructure asset management program for their systems. They began with their wastewa-

ter plant as a testing and development area to build integrated asset management systems and processes. The program needed to identify the criticality ranking of every system within the overall facility service area. They sought to discover what could put their mandated Level of Service at risk and to establish priorities for allocating their resources.

Response

In 2006 a criticality analysis was performed. Central to the overall success was the flexibility of the analysis to include evaluation categories important to the local client, such as safety, environmental risk, stakeholders, as well as capacity. The result was an analysis truly reflective of the client's local values.

The treatment plant was evaluated and an asset hierarchy was developed. Criticality analysis experts facilitated workshops with engineers, operations, and maintenance representatives from the city. The facility was broken into tens of functional systems, each designed to deliver a specific function, each comprising of hundreds of individual assets. This detailed approach using 100 percent coverage ensured identification of not only the critical systems but also the critical assets and sub-components in those systems to efficiently drill down to the items of concern.

Results

The analysis yielded some surprising results in addition to the anticipated areas of risk. Accurate rankings for all equipment yielded immediate returns by prioritizing for areas like engineering evaluation, maintenance and capital investment, operational attention, etc. Efficiency and payback gains were immediate and observable.

Gas Conditioning - A recent upgrade of the cogeneration plant brought particular focus to that part of the operation. More so, given that certain financial incentives and disincentives were put in place related to its service uptime, the overall importance of this system was deemed the most critical system. Upstream of the cogeneration plant, the gas-conditioning system cleans the gas and removes moisture to provide a gas quality nearly equal to distribution line natural gas. The gas conditioning system achieved a high ranking because of its collateral damage potential. Further, it had several points of failure, many of which would inhibit or stop the flow of gas to the cogeneration plant. The lead-time for the key vulnerable blower was 12-16 weeks.

The financial penalties associated with a failure here were prohibitive, and merely having a shelf spare of the blower mitigated this risk.

Substation Transformer - This identified system was a surprise to all participants. The transformer had been grandfathered into the treatment plant assets long ago from the electrical utility company. It had gone unnoticed by local management, had no record of inspection or condition, was historically assumed 'outside the fence', and was in fact unrecognized as part of the electrical transmission service to the plant. This substation was actually a single power feed to the old and lower portion of the plant receiving more than 4.8 million gallons of sewage per day by gravity. Failure of this substation would potentially result in 5 million gallons per day of raw sewage to the Columbia River. To exacerbate matters, a failure of the substation would likely damage the building next door that housed the emergency backup power breaker, effectively negating the use of backup power.

Fines associated with this event could be extremely high (hundreds of thousands of dollars) in addition to the negative public perception. A simple solution was not only to monitor and maintain the transformer, but also to arrange for a 24-hour replacement unit.

Service Vehicle - Because the entire process and all functions of the treatment plant were included in the analysis, vehicles were included and evaluated for criticality. The analysis revealed that a single front-end loader constituted multiple links in the flow of solids produced from the treatment process. Failure of the loader would stop solids flow, which would quickly backlog and impact the liquid treatment process significantly affecting effluent quality and capacity. This had not been identified as a risk area because vehicles had never been thought of as treatment process components.

The analysis revealed and quantified the requirements the loader was actually fulfilling. This provided all of the information and specifications needed to develop an alternative, which a simple advance agreement with a local rental vendor would adequately meet: a virtually no-cost mitigation to an otherwise major risk that previously had not been identified.

Telecom - main plant telecom and telephone systems were identified with a higher risk ranking than expected due to their integration in call out and emergency response systems, and one of the main treatment process units.

Summary
The criticality analysis far surpassed the original goal by identifying several areas of risk that had not been previously captured or recognized. Each had the potential to seriously affect the overall mission statement of the city's utility as well as result in costly fines and political fallout. Further, each was managed with relatively simple and low cost alternatives to reduce or eliminate the risks.

To meet the original goal, the analysis provided the ranking of all facility systems by priority, necessary to enable two things: the phased implementation of the larger asset management program, and the ongoing allocation of work and resources to proceed with maximum efficiency and efficacy.

Case Three: Refinery Boiler Feed Pretreatment System

Situation

A boiler feed water pretreatment system was due for an expansion and had undergone several design reviews, two HAZOP reviews, and several construction reviews. However, given the importance of this system within the refinery operation as well as being a key part of the refinery overall water reuse initiative, the refinery elected to commission a criticality analysis on the plant boiler feed water pretreatment system. The decision to perform a criticality analysis was also based, in part, on the success of the previous review methodology. However, since the system had also undergone some annual refurbishments and after 18 years of operation was thought to be fully 'known', there were decreased expectations that any previously unidentified issues would surface. This assumption proved to be false.

Response

As in the previous example, the success of this analysis again hinged on the flexibility to include not only areas such as safety, environmental, capacity, and up-time, but also commercial terms, liquidated damages, and contract terms. This proved to be a truly unique analysis with results reflective of more than just a process view, revealing the unique situation this system's risk profile posed within the larger context of the client operation.

The same steps were conducted as above, except in this case an asset registry had previously been generated as part of a HAZOP review. The database was imported for the analysis. Again, a team comprising various client experts was assembled with a criticality analysis expert facilitator. Inclusion of 100% of the overall process units in this functional area of the refinery again proved essential, as did leveraging the functional system approach. This enabled a more efficient means of identifying the critical systems and associated assets, saving time and money.

Results

The analysis did clarify and further define the generally known critical areas central to the overall mission. However, once again the analysis brought to the surface as yet uncovered risks inherent to the system. While the system was thought to be fully understood, neither the ranking of critical risk systems was as expected, nor was the discovery of the most critical systems. One system was a particular surprise to the investigating team and two other systems were elevated to a higher criticality than previously thought given the potential for overall system failure.

Brine System - Previous thinking had placed the highest risk on the actual softener units that had internal corrosion issues, valued at almost $1MM, which would impair capacity. However, the analysis showed that the failure of a $10K brine recharge system would bring the whole treatment facility to a full shutdown in less than a shift with no alternative or backup. This event would have a serious impact on the refinery operational cost, even possible reduction of boiler capacity, in addition to triggering contractual damages as a service provider to the refinery. The lead-time to replace the system was four weeks and so any unexpected downtime of the brine system would have been clearly unacceptable. The potential cost of the risk was hundreds of times that of the brine pump system cost.

As a consequence the pump system was evaluated for condition and severity of service load. The decision was made quickly to replace the pump with a new and more robust one.

Waste Lines Blockage – The waste lines had always been assumed a secondary consideration of the system as they were operated at low or ambient pressure, and thus had little attention focused on them. However, given the system configuration it was discovered that any potential blockage, via several mechanisms, outside the operational boundary area would result in a serious process upset and possible blowout of the main RO units, in addition to fouling of the membranes. Aside from the cost to repair and clean the membranes, the down time would be unacceptable to the refinery. The solution was again simple and inexpensive - enhanced monitoring and inexpensive relief valves - compared to the potential cost of the risk (over $100K).

Plant Air – A system that often went unnoticed, especially just outside the battery limit of the process unit, was the plant compressed air supply. Several of the key water conditioning and support backwash and cleaning operations are controlled by air-operated valves. Even partial failure of the air system via low pressure in this system could again severely impair the operation of the overall system, even to complete process failure. Once again the solution to reduce the risk profile was low cost versus the risk of a shut down; additional inspections and a simple pressure alarm were added.

Summary

Even though the system and its associated risks were thought to be fully understood, inclusion of contractual and commercial evaluation parameters highlighted relationships between process and commercial risks that had previously gone unnoticed. A true cost could then be assigned to those risks for a more comprehensive business risk evaluation. As part of the exercise, it was also easy to identify low cost and tangible solutions to mitigate those risks at a fraction of the risk cost, significantly reducing the cost to maintain and efficiently targeting capital and maintenance dollars.

About the Author

Tacoma Zach is owner and CEO of Uberlytics, experts in criticality analysis. With over two decades in operations under his belt, he now helps organizations discover what's most critical to their mission and use that information to optimize their asset management. Uberlytics provides unique and best-in-class criticality analysis facilitation and tools to asset intensive organizations like refineries, complex industry, power utilities, and municipal water and wastewater utilities.

Prior to assuming the leadership of Uberlytics, Tacoma held various executive roles at Veolia Water, most recently overseeing the Western US industrial operations, including refineries, production fields, remediation sites and airline maintenance facilities.

After finishing his Masters in Chemical Engineering at the University of Toronto, Tacoma launched his career running process studies and personally building pilot plants. In the two-plus decades since, his professional experience has included engineering and process design, leading DBO projects, muncipal and industrial plant commissioning and operations, business development and internationational and domestic business management and executive leadership. He has a unique blend of experience in both the municipal and industrial water and wastewater business, along with industrial operational experience including food processing, petroleum refineries and mining, among others.

Tacoma's breadth and depth of operational and business leadership experience uniquely positions him to understand asset management and reliability from both the perspective of operators and maintainers with responsibility for uptime, and the perspective of asset owners and business leaders with responsibility for the bottom line. Having had these responsibilities himself, Tacoma knows firsthand the value of a criticality analysis for almost every part of a business.

Tacoma holds Bachelors and Masters degrees in Chemical Engineering from the University of Toronto, is a licensed Professional Engineer in Ontario and Alberta, Canada, and a Certified Reliability Leader. He is committed to leading stakeholders to work together to deliver value from their assets and programs through doing the right things, for the right reasons, in the right order.

Uptime® Elements

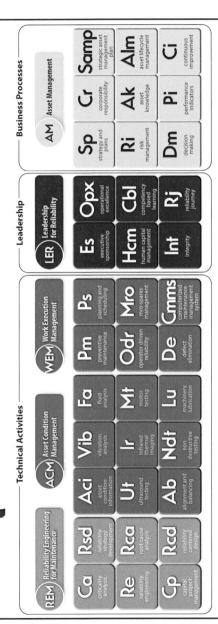

A Reliability Framework and Asset Management System™

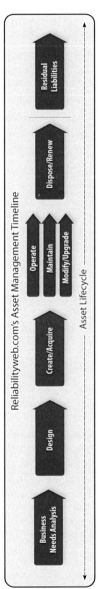

Reliabilityweb.com's Asset Management Timeline

reliabilityweb.com • maintenance.org • reliabilityleadership.com

Reliabilityweb.com® and Uptime® Magazine Mission: **To make the people we serve safer and more successful.** One way we support this mission is to suggest a reliability system for asset performance management as pictured above. Our use of the Uptime Elements is designed to assist you in categorizing and organizing your own Body of Knowledge (BoK) whether it be through training, articles, books or webinars. Our hope is to make YOU safer and more successful.

ABOUT RELIABILITYWEB.COM

Created in 1999, Reliabilityweb.com provides educational information and peer-to-peer networking opportunities that enable safe and effective reliability and asset management for organizations around the world.

ACTIVITIES INCLUDE:

Reliabilityweb.com® (www.reliabilityweb.com) includes educational articles, tips, video presentations, an industry event calendar and industry news. Updates are available through free email subscriptions and RSS feeds. **Confiabilidad.net** is a mirror site that is available in Spanish at www.confiabilidad.net.

Uptime® **Magazine** (www.uptimemagazine.com) is a bi-monthly magazine launched in 2005 that is highly prized by the reliability and asset management community. Editions are obtainable in both print and digital.

Reliability Leadership Institute® Conferences and Training Events (www.reliabilityleadership.com) offer events that range from unique, focused-training workshops and seminars to small focused conferences to large industry-wide events, including the International Maintenance Conference (IMC), MaximoWorld and The RELIABILITY Conference™ (TRC).

MRO-Zone Bookstore (www.mro-zone.com) is an online bookstore offering a reliability and asset management focused library of books, DVDs and CDs published by Reliabilityweb.com.

Association of Asset Management Professionals
(www.maintenance.org) is a member organization and online community that encourages professional development and certification and supports information exchange and learning with 50,000+ members worldwide.

A Word About Social Good
Reliabilityweb.com is mission-driven to deliver value and social good to the reliability and asset management communities. *Doing good work and making profit is not inconsistent*, and as a result of Reliabilityweb.com's mission-driven focus, financial stability and success has been the outcome. For over a decade, Reliabilityweb.com's positive contributions and commitment to the reliability and asset management communities have been unmatched.

Other Causes
Reliabilityweb.com has financially contributed to include industry associations, such as SMRP, AFE, STLE, ASME and ASTM, and community charities, including the Salvation Army, American Red Cross, Wounded Warrior Project, Paralyzed Veterans of America and the Autism Society of America. In addition, we are proud supporters of our U.S. Troops and first responders who protect our freedoms and way of life. That is only possible by being a for-profit company that pays taxes.

I hope you will get involved with and explore the many resources that are available to you through the Reliabilityweb.com network.

Warmest regards,
Terrence O'Hanlon
CEO, Reliabilityweb.com